WhO HOpS?

SCHOLASTIC INC.

New York   Toronto
London   Auckland
Sydney   Mexico City
New Delhi   Hong Kong

By
KATIE
DAVIS

To my husband, Jerry,
who has helped me make my dreams come true
(kenahora ptew, ptew)

ISBN 0-439-13363-7

12 11 10 9 8 7 6 5 4 3 2 1   9/9 0 1 2 3 4/0

Printed in the U.S.A.   24

First Scholastic printing, September 1999

Who
hops?

Frogs hop.

Rabbits
hop.

Kangaroos
hop.

Cows hop.

NO THEY DON'T!

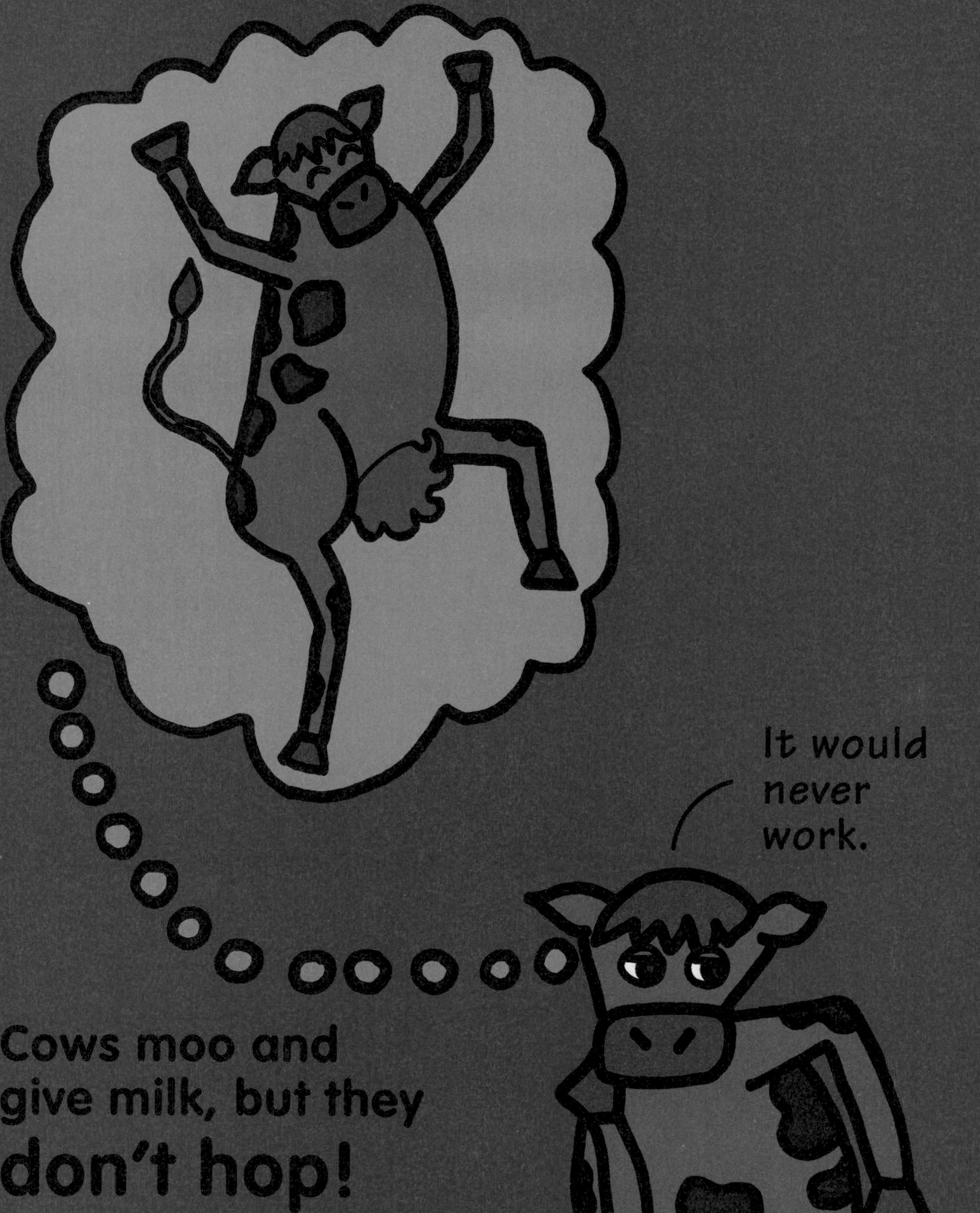

Cows moo and give milk, but they **don't hop!**

Birds fly.

Bats fly.

Flies fly.

Rhinos fly.

NO THEY DON'T!

Rhinos eat grass and take lots of baths, but they don't fly!

Salamanders slither.

Snakes
slither.

Snails slither.

Elephants slither.

NO THEY DON'T!

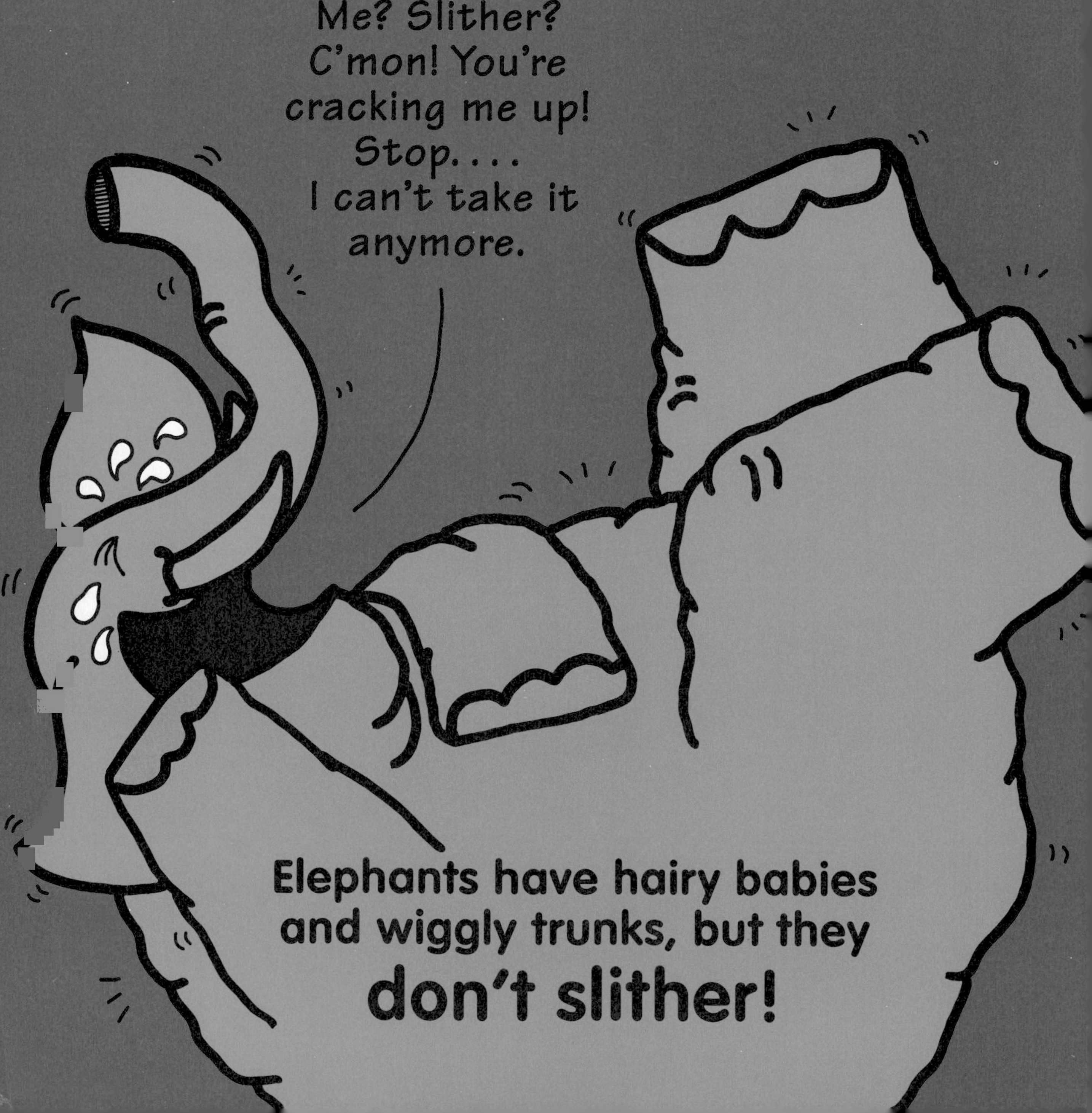

Elephants have hairy babies and wiggly trunks, but they

don't slither!

Goldfish swim.

Sharks swim.

Whales swim.

Anteaters swim.

NO THEY DON'T!

Anteaters eat ants and have long sticky tongues, but they **don't swim!**

I just ate, so I really shouldn't go swimming anyway.

Spiders crawl.

Crabs crawl.

Crocodiles
crawl.

Giraffes
crawl.

NO THEY DON'T!

Giraffes eat leaves and have really tall babies, but they

don't crawl!

You do!

I give enormous and heartfelt thanks
to my own personal superhero triumvirate:
Peggy Rathmann, my mentor and friend, who hooked me up with
Steven Malk, my genius agent, who got me to
Susan Schneider, my editor, who brought this book
to a whole other level.

Without the support and constant hounding
from my amazing critique group—
Rosi Dagit, Molly Ireland, Maria Johnson,
Ainslie Pryor, Pam Smallcomb, and Ann Stalcup—
this book would have been all wrong.

And if Benny and Ruby,
my spirited and sweet children,
hadn't played Who Hops? with me in the first place . . .
Well, you get the picture.

The illustrations in this book were done in pen-and-ink with pre-separated colors.
The display type and text type were set in Vag Rounded.
Designed by Linda Lockowitz